# THE MOUNTAINS OF MADNESS

BASED ON THE NOVEL
BY

*H. P.* **LOVECRAFT**

*At the* **Mountains** *of* **Madness**

---

*written and drawn by*
**ADAM FYDA**

IT IS 1932. THE LAST PREPARATIONS FOR THE SECOND ANTARCTIC EXPEDITION ARE UNDERWAY AT THE DOCKS OF THE BOSTON PORT.

EXCUSE ME, ARE YOU PROFESSOR HOWARD PYM?

EEE, YES?

PLEASE, YOU HAVE TO TAKE IT AND PROMISE ME YOU'LL READ IT BEFORE YOU REACH THE SOUTH POLE! I'M BEGGING YOU!

HELLO!? WHO ARE YOU? WHAT IS...?

ON 20TH AUGUST, ALMOST TWO YEARS AFTER THE FAMOUS FIRST ANTARCTIC EXPEDITION LED BY PROFESSOR WILLIAM DYER, TWO BARQUES – "ARKHAM" AND "MISKATONIC" SAILED AGAIN TO THE ANTARCTIC POLE.

THEIR ROUTE WAS TO BE THE SAME AS THE PREVIOUS EXPEDITION: THROUGH THE PANAMA CANAL, THEN SAMOA, WITH THE FINAL STOP IN TASMANIA TO LOAD UP, BEFORE TRAVELLING ON TO THE ROSS SEA.

BARQUE "ARKHAM", NOVEMBER 2, 1932

THE PANAMA CANAL BEHIND US – THE PACIFIC OCEAN BEFORE US.

SCORESBY, I'D LIKE TO TAKE ANOTHER LOOK AT THE MATERIALS FROM THE PREVIOUS EXPEDITION.

SURE, I HAVE THEM IN MY CABIN.

THAT'S ALL THAT DYER GAVE TO THE UNIVERSITY. IN ADDITION, I HAVE COLLECTED PRESS RELEASES AND LOGBOOKS.

DURING THE FIRST WEEKS OF THE JOURNEY THERE WAS ALWAYS SOMETHING TO DO: INVENTORY, SEGREGATING AND SECURING EQUIPMENT AND PROVISIONS. NOW I FINALLY HAD SOME TIME TO RE-EXAMINE THE RESEARCH FINDINGS AND REPORTS FROM WILLIAM DYER'S TRAGIC EXPEDITION.

76° 15'S
113° 10'E

November 24, 1930

January 22, 1931

| h. | |
|---|---|
| 4⁰⁰ | Lake takes off on three planes. |
| 6 ⁴⁵ | Lake reports he's landed 300 km north. He starts drillings. |
| 14¹⁰ | L. reports the discovery of many fossils. He decided to continue his flight to the east. |
| 15⁰⁰ | L. takes off and flight on. |

...neers J. Wul"

THE PLANES TOOK OFF, STORM CLOUDS ...RED ON THE HORIZON...

... SOON AFTER THAT, THE PLANES FLEW INTO A BIG SNOWSTORM...

...izzard.

...30

... THEY FLEW FOR OVER AN HOUR AND HARDLY SAW ANYTHING AROUND THEM...

...D SUDDENLY THE BLIZZARD STOPPED...

ONE OF THE PLANES WAS DAMAGED DURING THE SNOWSTORM...

... WHICH FORCED THE EXPEDITION TO LAND AND SET UP A CAMP ON A PLATEAU AT THE FOOT OF A NEWLY DISCOVERED MOUNTAIN CHAIN...

... DURING THE REPAIR OF DORNIER THEY STARTED DRILLING AND RESEARCHING...

... WHICH LED TO THE DISCOVERY OF A LARGE UNDERGROUND CAVE...

... FILLED WITH REMAINS AND FOSSILS FROM VARIOUS GEOLOGICAL ERAS...

... AS REPORTED BY LAKE IN HIS LATEST RADIO BROADCAST.

NOW WE'RE BREAKING UP THE RESEARCH OF A CAVE. THE SNOWSTORM IS COMING.

YOU MUST THEREFORE SECURE THE CAMP WELL — CATABATIC WINDS CAN BE VERY STRONG AND DANGEROUS.

SURE. CONTACT AFTER STORM. OVER AND OUT!

ADVERTISER

JANUARY 27. 1931

NO. 361

# TRAGEDY IN ANTARCTIC: LAKE'S EXPEDITIONS MEMBERS DIED IN SNOWSTORM

In a previous report we informed our readers about Professor Lake's expedition into the unexplored territories of Antarctica and the sensational discoveries made by him and his team there.

Two days ago, the radio station in Lake's camp was silent. William Dyer, the head of the expedition, decided to fly one of the planes to investigate the situation. Unfortunately, it turned out that the all-night snowstorm had completely devastated the camp. No one survived, only some of the excavations were rescued. Also the entrance to the underground cave was not found, the discovery of which was reported by Professor Lake a few days ago.

NOVEMBER 5, 1932, "ARKHAM'S" DECK

LISTEN TO ME SCORESBY – YOU'RE A BIOLOGIST, CAN YOU TELL ME SOMETHING MORE ABOUT THESE EXCAVATIONS FROM THE CAVE DISCOVERED BY LAKE?

OH THESE? THE MOST INTERESTING THING ABOUT THESE IS...

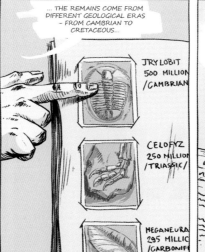

... THE REMAINS COME FROM DIFFERENT GEOLOGICAL ERAS – FROM CAMBRIAN TO CRETACEOUS...

JRY LOBIT 500 MILLION /CAMBRIAN

CELOFYZ 250 MILLION /TRIASSIC/

MEGANEURA 295 MILLIO /CARBONIF

... AND THEY ARE ALL MIXED TOGETHER AS IF THEY WERE FROM THE SAME ERA.

AS A GEOLOGIST, YOU KNOW THAT THIS DOESN'T HAPPEN.

YES – ORGANIC REMAINS FROM A PARTICULAR PERIOD CAN ONLY BE FOUND IN THE GEOLOGICAL LAYER FROM THAT PERIOD.

AND HERE IT LOOKS LIKE SOMEBODY PUT THEM ALL TOGETHER AND STORED THEM ALL TOGETHER.

LIKE IN A TOMB OR A MUSEUM...

EXACTLY!

I'VE NEVER FOUND DYER'S INTERPRETATION ABOUT IT. AND YET HE WAS A GEOLOGIST AND LEADER OF THIS EXPEDITION.

DYER WAS VERY SILENT ON HIS RETURN TO THE UNIVERSITY OF MISKATONIC...

... AND SOON AFTERWARDS RESIGNED FROM HIS PROFESSORSHIP, LEFT AND HID SOMEWHERE IN THE COUNTRYSIDE.

THE NEXT FEW WEEKS PASSED QUIETLY. ON 28TH DECEMBER 1932 WE SAILED FROM THE PORT OF HOBART, TASMANIA, THE LAST PART OF THE CRUISE AHEAD OF US.

ON JANUARY 9TH WE CROSSED THE POLAR CIRCLE, WHICH WAS CELEBRATED WITH THE TRADITIONAL POLAR BAPTISM CEREMONY.

THE FARTHER WE MOVED SOUTH, THE COLDER IT GREW, FORCING EVERYONE TO PULL THEIR WARM CLOTHES BACK ON.

AND I HAD THE OPPORTUNITY TO DISCOVER A FORGOTTEN NOTEBOOK GIVEN TO ME BY A STRANGER IN BOSTON PORT...

???

... WHICH I HAD INSTINCTIVELY PUT IN MY POCKET AND FORGOT ABOUT AMONG EVERYDAY DUTIES.

ONCE AGAIN, I WAS SINKING INTO THE HISTORY OF WILLIAM DYER'S EXPEDITION...

BILL! YOU HAVE TO SEE THIS! IT'LL CHANGE HISTORY WE KNOW TO DATE!

WE WERE DRILLING IN THE GEOLOGICAL STRATA OF THE PRECAMBRIAN PERIOD AND LOOK WHAT WE FOUND THERE! FOSSILS, DO YOU UNDERSTAND? THERE WERE NO COMPLEX LIFE FORMS YET!

HMMM... INTERESTING, BUT ARE YOU SURE IT'S NOT JUST A COINCIDENCE?

NO, WE'VE FOUND MORE OF THEM!

IF WE START EXPLORING AREAS FURTHER EAST, I'M SURE WE'LL FIND EVEN MORE!

LET ME TAKE THE PLANES, THE EQUIPMENT AND SOME PEOPLE. IF WE DON'T FIND ANYTHING, WE'LL BE BACK. SUCH AN OPPORTUNITY MAY NOT HAPPEN AGAIN.

OKAY. TAKE OFF TOMORROW AND WE'LL BE IN REGULAR RADIO CONTACT.

JANUARY 22, 1931, AT 2:10 P.M., AFTER THE FIRST DRILLING, LAKE DECIDED TO CONTINUE THE FLIGHT...

DYER! AS I EXPECTED, WE FOUND MORE PRINTS. THERE'S A VERY STRONG WIND, BUT WE'RE FLYING FURTHER EAST TO DO SOME MORE DRILLING THERE.

LAKE! IT'S TOO DANGEROUS! LAND AND RETURN TO BASE AS SOON AS IT CALMS DOWN! WE CAN'T AFFORD SUCH A RISK!

AFTER WHAT WE'VE FOUND, EVERY RISK PAYS OFF! OVER AND OUT.

JANUARY 23, 1931, AT 5:30 P.M., LAKE REPORTS THE DISCOVERY OF AN UNDERGROUND CAVE...

... THE EXCAVATIONS FROM THERE INDICATE AN EXTRAORDINARY CONTINUITY BETWEEN LIFE FORMS 300 MILLION YEARS AGO AND 30 MILLION YEARS AGO.

AND THAT ENDS THE MESSAGE TO "ARKHAM ADVERTISER". DYER, I WANT TO TELL YOU SOMETHING ELSE...

YES, I'M LISTENING, LAKE.

WE'VE FOUND SOMETHING OTHER THAN FOSSILS...

... GEDNEY AND I WENT DOWN TO THE CAVE AGAIN...

LET'S TAKE A CLOSER LOOK AT THOSE STALACTITES.

THERE'S A LOT OF THESE TRIANGULAR PRINTS IN HERE.

... OH, MY GOSH!

WHAT'S THAT!?

NOT STALACTITES FOR SURE...

WE HAVE TO TRY TO BRING IT TO THE SURFACE.

BUT THERE WAS NO CONTACT WITH LAKE THE NEXT DAY...

HELLO!? LAKE!? THIS IS BASE... OVER!

... OR EVER AGAIN.

WE NEED TO PREPARE TWO PLANES FOR FLIGHT. TOMORROW MORNING WE WILL FLY WITH DANFORTH, ATWOOD AND A FEW PEOPLE TO LAKE'S CAMP.

THE COORDINATES MATCH WHAT LAKE REPORTED! THE CAMP SHOULD BE SOMEWHERE HERE.

THESE MOUNTAINS, THEY'RE JUST LIKE LAKE DESCRIBED. THEY ARE PROBABLY HIGHER THAN THE HIMALAYAS!

LOOK DOWN THERE! THERE'S A CAMP!

HALLOO! LAKE?

HEY! HEY!?

STRANGE... THERE'S NO ONE HERE...

I THINK THAT WAS THE DOGHOMESTEAD THAT LAKE MENTIONED.

BUT WHERE ARE THE DOGS?

COMPLETELY DESTROYED...

I'LL CHECK IN THE TENTS...

OH NOO...!

ALL DEAD!

THEIR BODIES ARE ALL MIXED UP...

GOD, WHAT HAPPENED IN HERE...?

WE HAVE TO BURY THEM...

GEDNEY'S BODY ISN'T HERE. AND ONE OF THE DOGS, TOO.

WE HAVE TO LOOK FOR HIM! MAYBE HE'S HERE SOMEWHERE AND HE'S STILL ALIVE.

JANUARY 20, 1933, LANDING AND UNLOADING IN MCMURDO BASE.

SECURE THESE PACKAGES AND FINISH TODAY. IT'S ALMOST MIDNIGHT.

DURING THE ANTARCTIC SUMMER, IT STILL FEELS LIKE IT'S THE MIDDLE OF THE DAY.

BECAUSE THE SUN WON'T COME DOWN UNTIL MARCH.

WE HAVE TO GET USED TO THE FACT THAT IT'S STILL BRIGHT.

YES, IT'S AN UNNATURAL SITUATION FOR OUR ORGANISMS...

... AND SUCH ANOMALIES CAN CAUSE FATIGUE AND AFFECT THE PSYCHE – CAUSE NEUROSES AND EVEN HALLUCINATIONS.

AND NOT ONLY AMONG PEOPLE...

ARE YOU TALKING ABOUT THE DOGS?

AMONG OTHER THINGS. WE WERE JUST TALKING ABOUT LAKE'S LAST MESSAGE AND WHAT HAPPENED THERE AFTERWARDS...

WE SUSPECT THAT THESE FACTORS AND THE LONG PLANE JOURNEY COULD BE THE REASON WHY THE DOGS BROKE OUT FROM THE HOMESTEAD AND ATTACKED THEMSELVES AND THE PARTY.

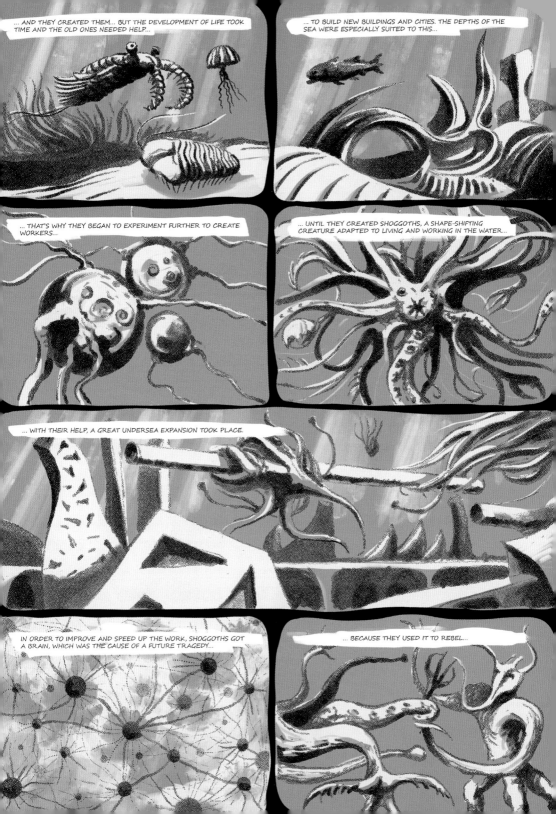

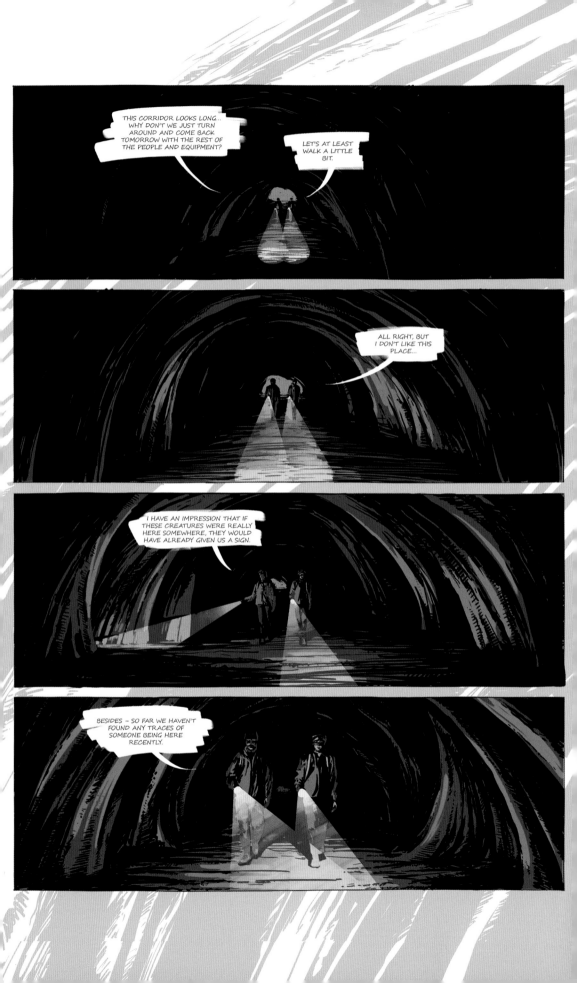

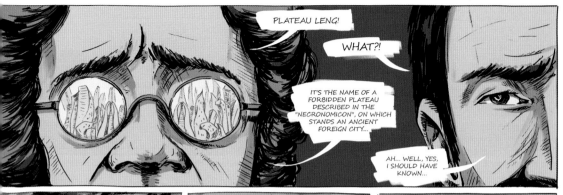

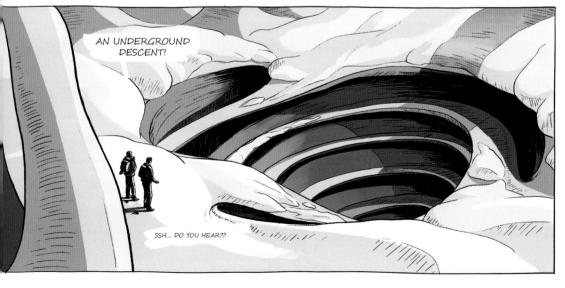

IS THAT A WIND I CAN HEAR?

SOUNDS MORE LIKE SOME KIND OF BIRD'S SONG.

BUT HERE? A BIRD? IMPOSSIBLE! I THINK IT'S THE WIND...

IT'S STOPPED... LET'S GO DOWN.

IF WE HAVE TO...

DANFORTH – DON'T COMPLAIN! YOU'RE DISCOVERING SOMETHING THAT NO ONE ELSE HAS EVER SEEN!

BESIDES, THERE'S NO TRACES OF ANYONE ELSE HERE BUT US.

IT'S A CORRIDOR...

THE ALIENS – WHY ARE THEY HERE TOO?

AND ALL THESE CREATURES FROM ANCIENT ERAS?

DOESN'T THIS REMIND YOU OF SOMETHING? DO YOU REMEMBER THE PHOTOS FROM THE UNDERGROUND CAVE THAT LAKE DISCOVERED?

AND MAYBE THESE, AS YOU SAY, "OLDER ONES", LIVED HERE WITH SOMEONE ELSE, SOMEONE WHO COLLECTED THE VARIOUS FORMS OF LIFE?

AND IT WAS THESE COLLECTORS WHO ATTACKED LAKE'S CAMP DURING THE SNOWSTORM AND TOOK THEIR TROPHIES HERE?

SHH... YOU HEAR THAT NOISE.?

LIKE WATER OR WAVES? WE HAVE TO CHECK IT OUT.

I DON'T... PLEASE, DO NOT GO ANY FURTHER... LET'S GO BACK!

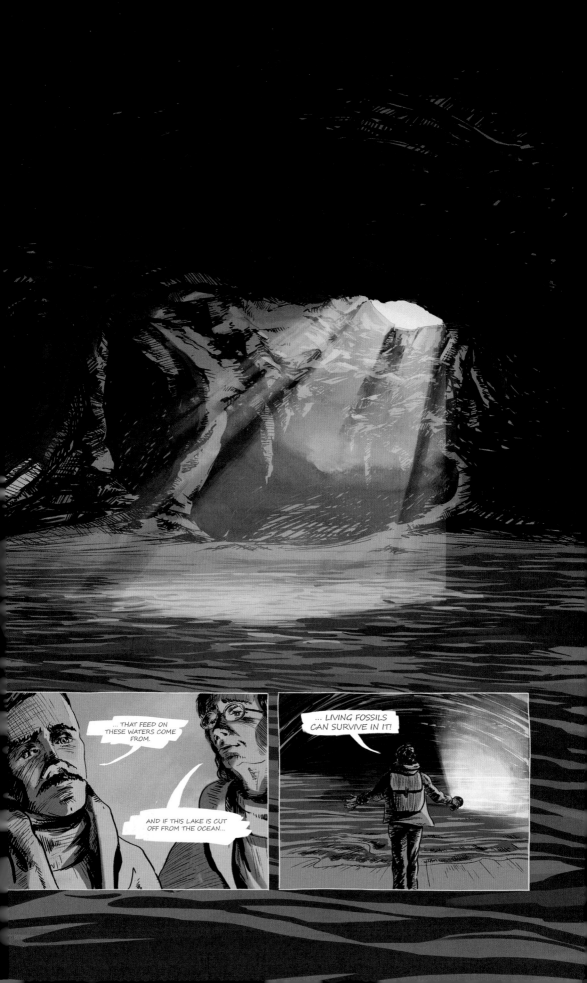

RUN!

WHATTT... IS... IT!?

A SHOGGOTH! HE... CAN'T TAKE... LONG... WITHOUT WATER!

END OF THE TUNNEL!

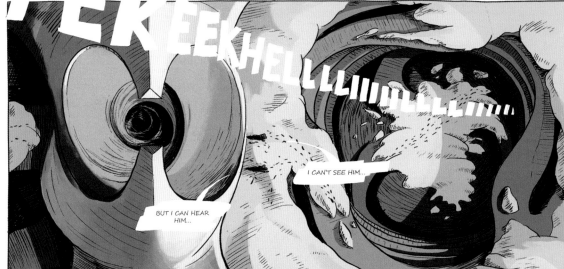

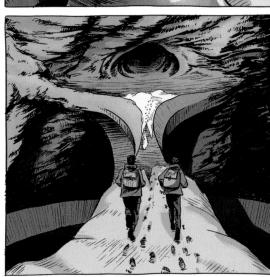

DANFORTH! ARE YOU OK?

NOOOAAAUUUULI-LI-TEKE-LIII!

HEY! CALM DOWN! IT'S OVER – WE'RE GETTING OUT OF THIS DAMN PLACE. AND EVERYTHING WILL BE FINE...

I THINK THE SHOGGOTH, OR WHATEVER IT WAS, DIED BURIED UNDERGROUND.

NOW YOU HAVE TO GET A GRIP – WE'LL ONLY GET DOWN TO THE CAMP TOGETHER.

I'LL TRY...

THERE! OUR PLANE!

BUT... BUT THERE ARE NO TENTS!

ON FEBRUARY 1, 1933, A SMALL PLANE ASCENDED INTO THE AIR AND HEADED SOUTH...

... CARRYING ONLY TWO PASSENGERS ON BOARD.

A MONTH LATER, A LONG, POLAR NIGHT FELL, AND
THE MOUNTAINS OF MADNESS WERE DROWNED IN THE DARKNESS.

FEBRUARY 1959, 78°21' S LONGITUDE AND 106° 50' E LATITUDE, SOVIET RESEARCH STATION "VOSTOK".

COMRADE PROFESSOR! I HAVE THE RESULTS OF THE SLOT PROFILING!

FINALLY! COME ON, COME ON, COME ON!

PLEASE, COMRADE CAPICA.

DO YOU SEE THIS DATA HERE? DO YOU KNOW WHAT IT MEANS?

AN UNDERGROUND CAVE? AND IT'S HUGE. BUT THESE HERE? I DON'T KNOW...

IT'S WATER! A HUGE UNDERGROUND LAKE...

THE END

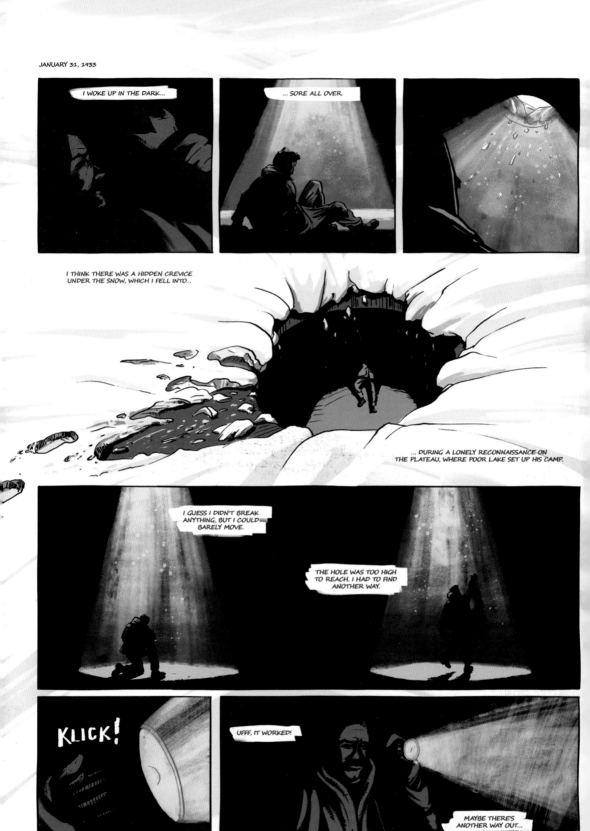

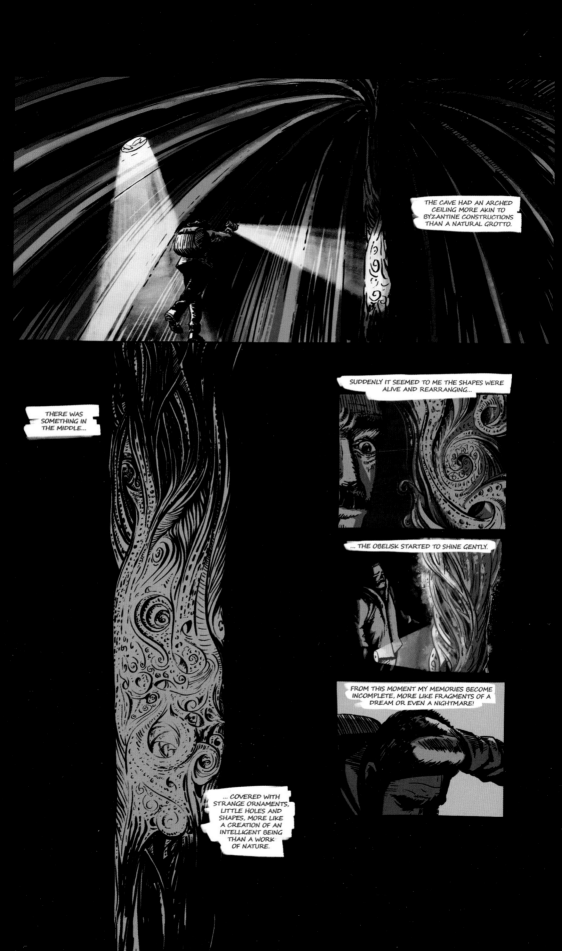

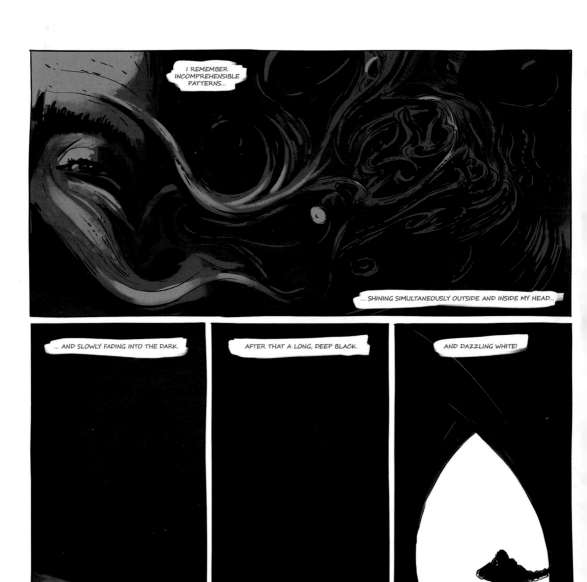

# THANK YOU

A Struggling Cartographer | Aad van der Valk | Aarne & Linda | Adam JOFFRAIN | Adam T Nowicki | Alan olson | Alex Hopton | Alex Marks | Alfie Kentesber | Alistair Gilmour – Enthusiast Of All Madness | Alycsa DeMarinis | Amanda K Smith | Anders Freder | Anders Stryhn-Johnsen | Andre | Andreas Woetzold | Andreea Alexandra | Andres Olguin | Andrew Brown | Andrew Fachau | Andrew Kottke | Andy MacDonald-Rice | Andy Perry | Anthony Francis | Antonio P. Nascimento | Antonio Wronski | Aria R. Ford | Arnaud Vajda | Arnold Huhndorf | Arthur Castro | Austin C Appleby | Avery Davenport | Avgerinos Konstantinos | Bad Tony | Baron Jason Rudolph Von Beck VII | Bashdown | Beau Oehlenschläger | Benny Guzman | Bill Birks | Billy Coghill | Bo Christiansen | Bobby Derie | Bonnie L Morse | Brandon Thomas The Silver Key Lounge | Brandon Viruet | Brian Robson | Bryan Castor | Bryan Koepp | Bryce Stoddart | Byron "Baragoon" Crane | C Anders T Olsson | C.R.S | Captain Orwell | Carl W Bishop | Carlos Mateus | Chad S. Fujioka | Charles Moulton | Charles Wilkins | Charlie Markwick storyteller and poet | Chris Call | Chris Chain | Chris Grummel | Chris Guidorizzi | Christie Grahame | Christopher Alshammar | Colin Oaten | Connor Shields | Craig D Hewitt | Curtis Reet | Dale Rodney Kent | Damon Schofield | Dane Northrup | Daniel Crosmun | Danniel A Navarrete | Darin Hlavaz | Darin Ross Stater | Darren James Longhorn | David Cunning | David Gopsill | David J Boocock | David Jones | David Lars Chamberlain | David Laslett | David Lowder | Denise Jennekens | Devilskebab | Dillan Holland | Dr. Georg F. Bischof | Dr. Michael A. Feldman | Drew W. Wheeler | Duncan Sandilands | Dustin Cissell | Dylan "Caligula" Distasio | Egoitz Uribeetxebarria | Eirik Holsæter | Elias Eliot | Elliott "Kip" Kipper | Eoin Murray | Eric Jennings | Eric Smith | Eric Zdilla | Erik Poulsen | Esapekka Eriksson | Ezra and Soren Rodriguez | Felipe de Jesús Hernandez | Felix & Flynn Dreher-East | Fenric Cayne | fess Azmi | Francesco Tehrani | Francisco Alejandro Morales | Francisco Plasencia Losada | Frank H Bustamante III | Fritz Herbert | G | G R Jordan EOD acolyte | Gary Moring | Gary Reeves | Gavin Call | Geoff G Turner | George Koumoutsos | Gextroll | Glee Gamers | Gordon Brown | Graeme Puttock | Graeme Rigg | Greg Heitz | Gregg Marcus | gsmarvedson | Gunnlaugur Thor | Hallur "Litli Trölli" Hallsson | Hans Johansson | Henning Herbert | Howard Kistler | Hunter BOYD-LOWEN | Ian D Rule | Igor Melnikov aka Meligan | Igor Piatek | Ina Alexandria Gur | Iñaki Mtz. de Marigorta | J&L Candalino | J3NCRYPT10N | Jace Chretin | Jackalgirl | James Anthony | James Coote | James Morphew | James Mummert | Jason Epstein | Javi G.M. | Jeff Galinski | Jeff Weber | Jenifur "JeniSkunk" Charne | Jérémy "Barbare" Noyé | Jeremy D. Wells | Jeremy Minett | Jerry B. Pierce | Jim Phillips | Joab Stie | Joe Pace | Joel Southard | Joerg Sterner | Joey Roa | John "AcesofDeath7" Mullens | John Grayson | John H. Simmons | John Mulligan | Johnny F. Normal | Jon Barrett | Jon Moseby | Jonas Andersson | Jonny Jones | Jordan Thompson | Joseph Bosner | Joshua Centeno | Juris L Purins | Justin Beard | Justin C' de Baca | Justin Tsantsa | Kael Thomas | Kari Salorenko | Kasper L. Hansen | Keely Taylor | Keith Woodson | Ken Brandt | Kenny Endlich | Kerr Griffin | Kevin J Donachie | Kevin Oviedo | Kevin Sawall | Kjetil André Fon Østby | Knievel MacEvil | Krisjan Lie | Kristijan Krpina | Kristos Pericleous | Krzysztof K | Kyle James | Lauren Pereira | Lee Werrin | leebigh | Lewis Griffiths | Librinpillole | Lionel the bass player | Lord Carlos 'Cato' Fabri | Lorenz Thor | Louise Lee | Lu770 P3rP37u0 | M. T. Hall | Mancia Keglevich von Carcosa | Marc Aymi Montané | Marc Barkman-Astles | Marc Thorpe | Marcos Ramos | Marielle Birks | Mariposa Hernandez | Mark "Squircifer" Napier | Mark Byzewski | Mark Newman | Mark Pearce | Mark Stanislawski | Marten van der Leij | Martin Cattroll | Martin Jameson | Martin Metzler | Martin White | Mary Gaitan | Máté Gyor | Matthew Cooper | Matthew T. Carroll | Matthieu de Ronde | Michael "erzengel" Probst | Michael Angarone | Michael Bob Petersen | Michael Holzhausen | Michael PASCUITO-BELAC | Michail Dim. Drakomathioulakis | Michel Klaus | Mickey Twyford | Mike & Tom – Red Duke Games | Mike Burke | Mikey Tynemouth | Mister E | Monty Brandenberg | Mr C Moses | Nathan Biewer | Nathan Ladd | Nathan Libby | Nathaniel S. Venzor | Neil Dickie | Neil Westlake | Nick "the old one" Williams | Nick Lockwood | Nicodemonous | Noa Simon Schäfer | Noel Keating | nolongerhuman | Osamah A. Albaghdadi | Osawe Whitelock | Oyvind Wiestad | P. Malmberg | Paivi Sahi-Aura | Parker Lucy | Patrick Thomas Nunnery | Paul & Laura Trinies | Paul C. Grimaldi | Paul Carroll | Paul Grixti | Paul Saarnak | Pearce Haley | Pekka Poukka | Peter Anders | Philip Borgkvist | Priyum Patel | R. D. Peacock | Rafael Jasso | Rahkeem Wright | Rahul Soni | Ralf Steinberg | Ralph Redfern | Rama N. Toulon | Raul Arias Philippi | Remco Verbeek | Renal Wizard | Ricardo Alting | Rich Laux | Richard Eaton | Richard Franklin | Rik Moore | Robert "Trebor" Carey | Robert Greathouse | Robert Muncy | Robert Sambuco Michaud | Ronny Anderssen | Rui Poças | Ruki and Bernd | Russell Lim | S. W. Nikola | Samantha St. John | Sammy G. | Samuel Fowler | Sandra H. Bruel – BeSLN | Sanne STIJVE | Sarah | Saul Grabin | Scantronth | Scarlett Letter | Scott Bartlett | Scott Bishop | Séamus Murphy | Séan Harry | Seán Johnst | Seb Fabre | Sebastian – Phobos_s – Tworek | Sebastian Alonso | Sebastian Schramm | Sebastian Suarez | Selma H | Shane "Asharon" Sylvia | Shaun MacLeod | Shawn Howerton | Simon Hogg | Simon Skou Snoghøj | Simon T-W | skadooshmaster | SLUGBAIT | Stacy Roberts (Ayailla) | Stefan Mazetti | Stephan Roslen | Stéphane Huart | Stephen Collins Jr | Stephen Duke Lord | Stephen John Wintle | Stephen Stewart | Stuart Warren | Svein jørgensen | Sven Wiese | Tailen | Tatiana Martinez | Tequila | The Rappley Family | TheHoboMagician | Théodaisios | Thomas Barclay | Thomas Buettner | Thomas Mueller | Thomas Siel | Thorgal Kristensson | Tibor von Mueller | Tim 'Aardvark' Meakins | Tim Lonegan | Tim Rouse | Timon Tomas | TJ Decay | Tony Buckley | Tony Herman | Torrie Rh | Tyler Baker | Tyler H Martin | Ulf Andersson swe | VEXAGRAM | Vicente Sampedro | W David Lewis | Wade Mans | Ward Dufraing | William Jarrett | William Ridgway | Xymon Owain | Yakov Petyavich | Yann ALIDOR | Your Friend Nate